Guitar
Scales & Arpeggios

Grades 6–8

Why practise scales?

Welcome to this book of technical requirements for guitar. Practising scales, arpeggios and other patterns plays an essential part in developing a guitarist's skills. Time devoted to these exercises within each practice session will improve many aspects of technique, such as hand positions, co-ordination and left-hand shifts. In addition, the sense of key and pattern acquired through familiarity with scales and arpeggios has several benefits: it speeds up the learning of new pieces, helps develop evenness of line, quality of tone and good legato playing, builds aural awareness, and increases familiarity with the geography of the fingerboard.

For the exam

Tempo
The candidate should aim for a tempo that achieves a clean, uniform tone and a rhythmic flow without undue accentuation. Recommended minimum speeds are printed in this book for each requirement.

Tirando/apoyando
'Fingers-only' scales must be played both *tirando* (free stroke) and *apoyando* (rest stroke). The *tirando* stroke is expected for all other requirements.

Choice of fingering
The fingerings given in this book, while not compulsory, are strongly recommended. However, the examiner will not comment on the choice of fingering unless it interferes with the performance. Any combination of alternating right-hand fingers may be used for the 'fingers-only' scales; those involving the ring finger are no longer compulsory.

On the day
The examiner will usually ask for at least one of each type of requirement set for the grade. These must be played from memory.

The examiner will be looking for:
- confident, controlled and consistent tone across the pitch range
- an even and positive sense of rhythm
- accurate, fluent and, above all, legato realization of the different scales, arpeggios and other patterns.

Notes on the requirements & practical points

Interval scales
Scales in sixths, tenths, octaves and thirds are to be played together as well as broken. The ability to play in this range of intervals is fundamental to a harmonic understanding of guitar music and a thorough working knowledge of the fingerboard. It also greatly assists the development of left-hand positioning and finger independence, as well as enhancing the overall co-ordination of the hands. Playing interval scales broken can be approached in the same way as playing them together, i.e. with right-hand thumb and finger planted simultaneously with every crotchet beat.

Arpeggios and broken chords

All arpeggios (including dominant and diminished sevenths) are to be played with no over-ringing of adjacent notes. This is easily achieved by following the given left-hand fingerings, which exclude half-barrés and open strings.

By contrast, broken chords are to be played with notes over-ringing – a natural consequence of each triad covering three separate strings. It is not necessary for the candidate to damp notes that ring beyond the triad.

Distinguishing between over-ringing and non-over-ringing in this way is invaluable in helping the student understand the function of different musical elements, e.g. whether a specific arpeggiated passage is part of a melodic line or an accompanying harmonic texture.

Left-hand fingering

- Position signs (in Roman numerals) are the primary source of information; these are complemented by occasional left-hand finger numbers and string numbers.

Right-hand fingering

- For three-octave scales, the pattern ♪♪♪ ♪♪♪ has been chosen so that the rhythmic emphasis shifts between alternating right-hand fingers, such that if, for example, the first group of three quavers are played *im i*, then the second group will be played *m im*. This pattern promotes the development of right-hand rhythmic control and flexibility.

- The recommended right-hand fingerings for arpeggios (as well as dominant and diminished sevenths) have been chosen to work in tandem with the given left-hand fingerings and are largely determined by the occurrence and frequency of string crossings. They are designed to encourage a stable right-hand position and to explore a variety of thumb and finger combinations that reflect as closely as possible how passages such as these might be played in actual pieces.

Reference must always be made to the syllabus for the year in which the exam is to be taken, in case any changes have been made to the requirements.

Contents

Grade 6

SCALES

Fingers only / *tirando* and *apoyando*

Two octaves, ♩ = 112

Three octaves, ♩. = 76

CHROMATIC SCALE

Fingers only / *tirando* and *apoyando*

Two octaves, ♩ = 112

starting on C

INTERVAL SCALES

Together *and* **broken** / *tirando*

One octave, ♩ = 96

C major in thirds

together

broken

F major in tenths

together

broken

AB 3414

B minor harmonic in sixths

together

broken

G minor melodic in octaves

together

broken

BROKEN CHORD

With over-ringing / *tirando*

One octave, ♩. = 72

B♭ major

ARPEGGIOS

Without over-ringing / *tirando*

Two octaves, ♩. = 63

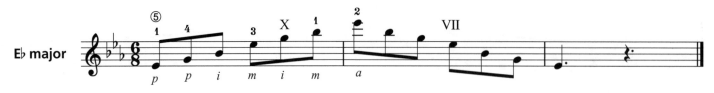

E♭ major

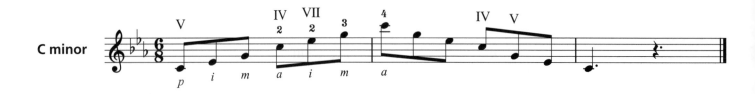

C minor

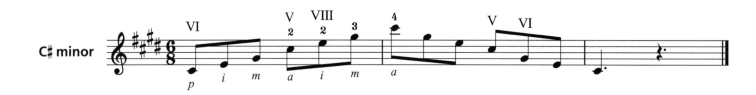

C♯ minor

Three octaves, ♩. = 63

E major

AB 3414

DOMINANT SEVENTH

Without over-ringing / *tirando*

Two octaves, ♩ = 96

DIMINISHED SEVENTH

Without over-ringing / *tirando*

Two octaves, ♩ = 96

* After the F is played, the open G in the previous bar should be damped so as to ensure correct harmonic resolution.

Grade 7

SCALES

Fingers only / *tirando* and *apoyando*

Two octaves, ♩ = 126

Ab major

B major

D minor melodic

D minor harmonic

G♯ minor melodic

G♯ minor harmonic

AB 3414

Three octaves, ♩. = 84

F major

F minor melodic

F minor harmonic

CHROMATIC SCALE

Fingers only / *tirando* and *apoyando*

Three octaves, ♩. = 84

starting on E

INTERVAL SCALES

Together *and* broken / *tirando*

One octave, ♩ = 104

D minor harmonic in octaves

together

broken

C minor melodic in tenths

together

broken

Two octaves, ♩ = 104

C major in sixths

together

broken

(Two octaves, ♩ = 104)

G major in thirds

together

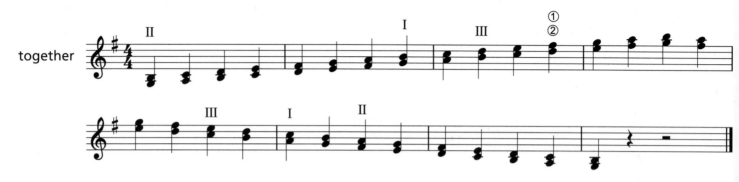

broken

BROKEN CHORD

With over-ringing / *tirando*

Two octaves, ♩. = 80

G minor

ARPEGGIOS

Without over-ringing / *tirando*

Two octaves, ♩. = 69

Ab major

B major

D minor

G# minor

Three octaves, ♩. = 69

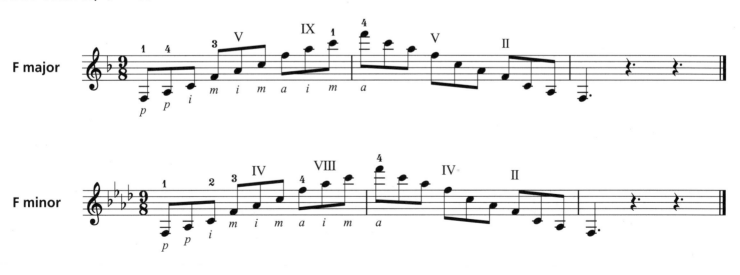

F major

F minor

DOMINANT SEVENTH

Without over-ringing / *tirando*

Three octaves, ♩ = 104

DIMINISHED SEVENTH

Without over-ringing / *tirando*

Three octaves, ♩ = 104

Grade 8

SCALES

Fingers only / *tirando* and *apoyando*

Two octaves, ♩ = 144

Db major

Bb minor melodic

Bb minor harmonic

Eb minor melodic

Eb minor harmonic

Three octaves, ♩. = 96

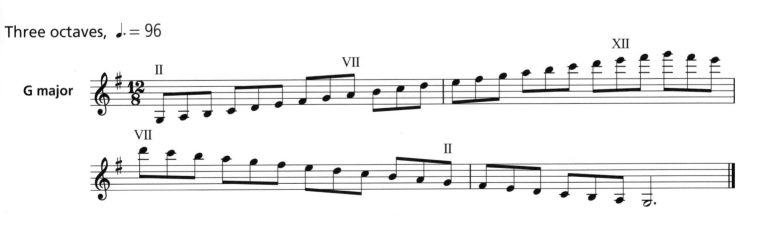

G major

(Three octaves, ♩. = 96)

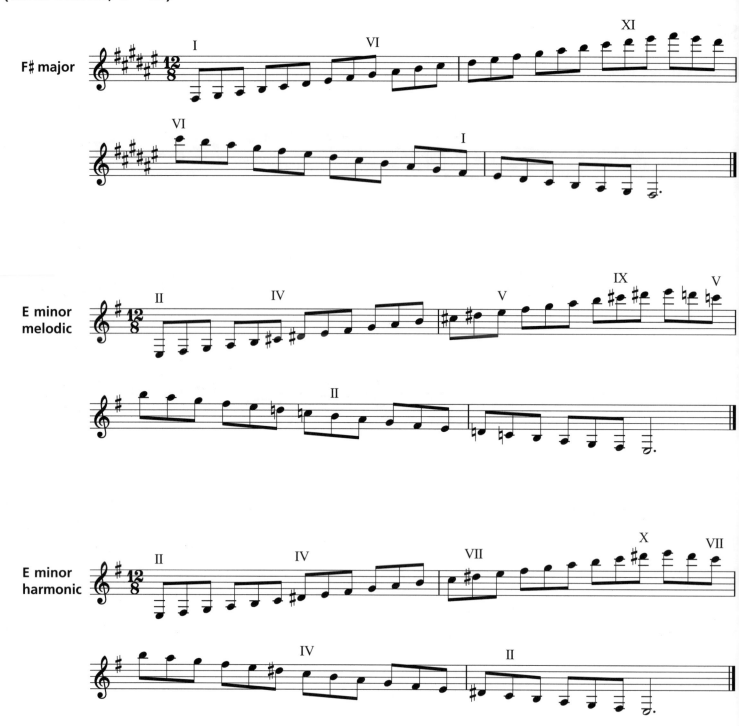

F# major

E minor melodic

E minor harmonic

CHROMATIC SCALE

Fingers only / *tirando* and *apoyando*

Three octaves, ♩. = 96

starting on F

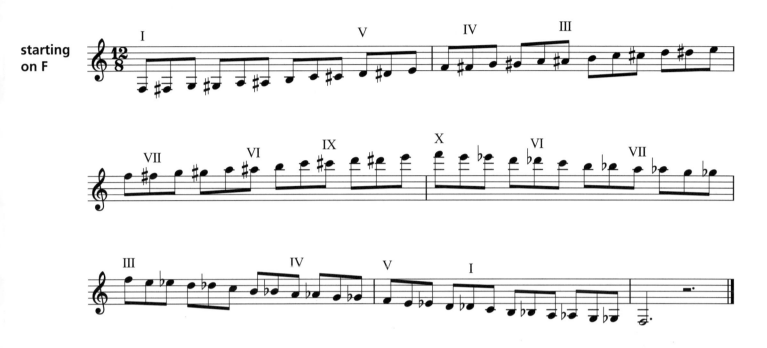

INTERVAL SCALES

Together *and* **broken** / *tirando*

One octave, ♩ = 116

D major in tenths

together

broken

Two octaves, ♩ = 116

A major in thirds

together

broken

G minor melodic in sixths

together

broken

F♯ minor harmonic in octaves

Chromatic scale in octaves, starting on E

and broken (see next page)

broken

BROKEN CHORDS

With over-ringing / *tirando*

Two octaves, ♩. = 88

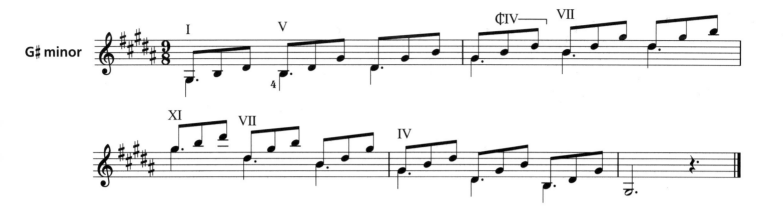

G# minor

ARPEGGIOS

Without over-ringing / *tirando*

Two octaves, ♩. = 76

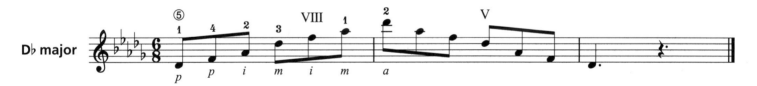

Db major

Bb minor

Eb minor

Three octaves, ♩. = 76

G major

F♯ major

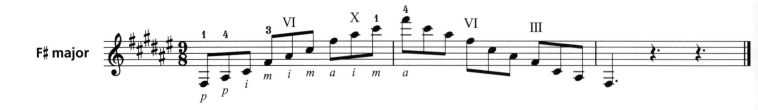

E minor

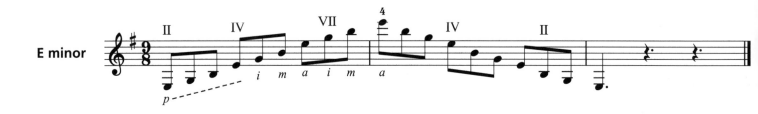

DOMINANT SEVENTHS

Without over-ringing / *tirando*

Three octaves, ♩ = 116

in the key of C

in the key of B♭

AB 3414

DIMINISHED SEVENTHS

Without over-ringing / *tirando*

Three octaves, ♩ = 116

starting
on G

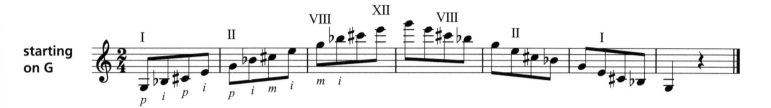

starting
on F

Printed in England by Caligraving Ltd, Thetford, Norfolk